KING ST.

Set Two
BOOK 4

Dave Goes to College

Dave Goes to College
King Street: Readers Set Two - Book 4
Copyright © Iris Nunn 2014

Text: Iris Nunn
Editor: June Lewis
Illustrations: Pip Jones and Marta Kwasniewska

Published in 2014 by Gatehouse Media Limited

ISBN: 978-1-84231-119-6

British Library Cataloguing-in-Publication Data:
A catalogue record for this book is available from the British Library

Dave lives at number six.
He lives with Jill.

He stays at home all day.
He has a bad back.
He watches TV and sleeps.
He gets fed up.

He spoke to Gwen
from number eleven.

"Why don't you go to college?"
she said.
"Go along and ask."

So Dave went along
to the college.
He asked about courses.

"What will it cost?" he asked.

"It is free," he was told.

So he decided to do
a computer course
and a literacy course.

"We'll get a computer," said Jill.
"You can go on the internet.
You can write letters.
You can e-mail your children.
You watch TV too much."

So now Dave goes to college
twice a week.

He goes on Monday mornings
and he goes on Thursday afternoons.

He likes it.
It gets him out of the house.
He has made new friends
and he is learning new skills.

Well done, Dave!